MOOSE MOMENTS

SILENT "E"

by Jacqueline Vinesse

Illustrated by Elizabeth Taylor

MOOSE MOMENTS: SILENT "E"

Written by Jacqueline Vinesse

Illustrated by Elizabeth Taylor

Edited by Charles Taylor, Janet Jones, Terri Tamres

Cover Image: Elizabeth Taylor

Layout: Elizabeth Taylor, Janet Jones, Dan Mackey

© 2010 Moose Materials
ISBN-13:978-1461089797
ISBN-10:1461089794

About Moose Moments

The aim of Moose Moments is to provide the teacher or parent with a resource for the reinforcement of the various phonograms, syllable types, and spelling rules encountered by the student who is learning to read and write.

A major influence behind this series of books is the organizational system of the Orton-Gillingham approach. This approach has been designed to increase reading success in the struggling reader, notably by arranging the structure of the English language into a sequence of increasing complexity which is then systematically taught. While this series can be used to provide practice for the struggling reader, it is not limited to the student who is experiencing difficulties. Instead, we feel that anyone faced with the task of grasping the complexities of English could benefit from this collection of stories and poems.

Each book consists of a number of stories and poems that have been written to exemplify a particular phonogram, syllable type, or spelling rule. To facilitate instruction, a definition of the concept targeted by each book is provided adjacent to the table of contents. In addition, each story is followed by a list of words that may not be recognized by the student, either because they typically occur later in the sequence, or because they are irregular words. (If required, these words can be given directly to the student.) We have also included a small number of definitions, essentially to serve as a quick reference for the teacher or parent.

There are a number of ways in which Moose Moments can be used: as practice reading material, as generators of word lists pertaining to a particular concept, or as a means to explore other areas underpinning linguistic competence such as rhyme, rhythm, and word play. In our view, however, one of the most important ways this collection can be used is in promoting the idea that reading can be fun!

TARGETED CONCEPT

SILENT "E"

A silent-e syllable ends in a vowel-consonant-silent-e. The vowels in these syllables represent the "long " sound. The silent "e" sounds are: "a-e " = /ā/ as in safe, "e-e" = /ē/ as in Pete, "i-e" = /ī/ as in pine, "o-e" = /ō/ home, and "u-e" = /ū/ as in mule.

Note: The following high frequency words appear repeatedly in these stories, allowing readers to have extensive practice with the words: *he, she, we, be, what, that, then, when, this, that, to, too, go, once, there, very, would, could, said*

TABLE OF CONTENTS

TATE THE SNAKE
WHO ATE TOO MUCH

Once there was a snake named Tate. He loved food. When Tate woke up, he felt very hungry. Then all day long, Tate just ate and ate and ate.

Tate the Snake ate mice -- but he did not stop there. If Tate came upon cake, he ate it. If Tate came upon a candy cane, he ate it. If Tate came upon grapes, he ate them. Even if Tate came upon a plate of stale food, he still tasted it.

There was a problem. Tate was getting fat. He was getting so fat that there was less space in the cage that he slept in. When Tate's doctor said he must go on a diet, Tate made a face. He said he would hate to do that.

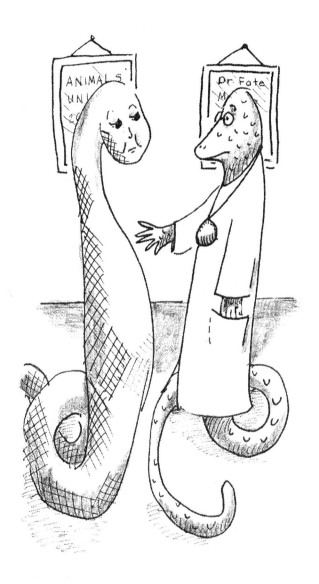

Then one day Tate's sister, Kate, came to visit. It was almost time for Kate's wedding and she asked Tate to be the best man. She made Tate try on his best cape for the wedding. Poor Tate! He was so fat that his cape did not fit him. All it did was hang on his back and make him look silly.

"What can I do?" said Tate. "I would hate to look like an ape at Kate's wedding!" So Tate the Snake went on a diet. He stopped eating candy canes. He stopped eating cake. He just ate mice and a bit of green kale.

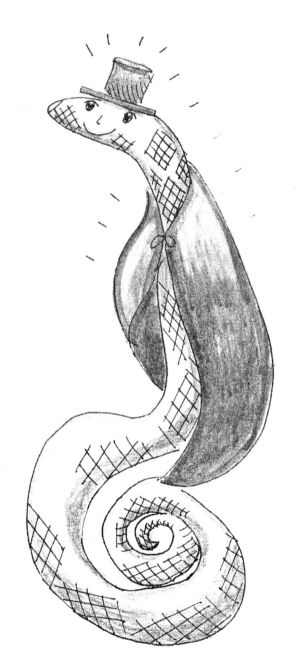

Before long, Tate was not fat. In fact, he was as slim as a rake and looked good in his cape. When the day of the wedding came, Tate shaved, put on his cape, and went off to church.

Then, when Tate the Snake came to the gate of the church, he met Kate's pal, Jane. She was a very cute snake. Before long, Jane and Tate were sharing a plate of wedding cake and planning a date!

TATE THE SNAKE
WHO ATE TOO MUCH

WORDS TO KNOW

<u>High Frequency Decodable Words</u>

he, try, all, almost, for, church, green, eating, day, food, poor, good, look, sister, silly, candy, doctor, hungry, even, before, sharing

<u>Note</u>: If c or g are followed by e, they usually make their soft sound as in **mice, face, space** and **cage**.

<u>High Frequency Irregular Words</u>

what, put, said, very, one, once, there, would, loved, guess

<u>Definitions</u>

diet – *when people eat less to lose weight*

kale – *green, leafy vegetable*

rake – *garden tool, often used to gather leaves*

PETE THE ATHLETE
WHO WENT TO CRETE

Pete was a boy who was very good at sports. His pals called him Pete the Athlete. Pete could run, jump, and swim better than the rest of his class.

When Pete was ten, he and his dad went on a trip to Crete. Pete met a boy from Sweden named Steve. Steve was also a very good athlete.

When Pete and his dad went to the beach, Pete would play games with Steve. The boys liked to compete to see who could swim better, dive better, kick the ball better, and run faster on the sand.

All too soon, the last day of the trip came. It was Christmas Eve and time for Pete and his dad to go home. Pete and Steve were very sad. They felt the days would not be complete if they could not compete.

When Pete got back home, he wrote a letter and sent it to Steve in Sweden. In the letter, he wrote:

Dear Steve,

It was a lot of fun to be in Crete. My dad said he will take me on a trip to Sweden soon. I hope we can meet, or maybe you can come here.

Sincerely,

Pete

Then Steve wrote back to Pete.

Dear Pete,

You are my best pal and such a good athlete. I hope we

can still meet and compete one of these days.

Sincerely,

Steve

After that, Pete and Steve wrote lots of letters. They are
still good athletes and meet whenever they can. Pete and Steve
are very glad they went to Crete!

PETE THE ATHLETE
WHO WENT TO CRETE

WORDS TO KNOW

<u>High Frequency Decodable Words</u>

he, go, all, ball, called, for, sports, see, meet, beach, day(s), play, good, too, soon, boy, after, faster, better, letter, dear, wrote, also, maybe, whenever, sincerely

<u>High frequency Irregular Words</u>

who, very, could, would, come, one, they, said, you, Christmas

<u>Definitions</u>

athlete – *someone who is good at sports*
Crete – *an island in the Mediterranean*
Sweden – *a country in Northern Europe*
compete – *to try to win against someone*

SPIKE THE MITE
WHO HAD A RIDE ON A BIKE

Spike was a mite who liked to be on Jimmy's dog. When Jimmy took his dog outside, Spike went too. When Jimmy took his dog inside, Spike went too. Sometimes, when Jimmy took his dog in the rain, Spike could get quite wet and cold. Most of the time he kept snug as a bug on Jimmy's dog. Spike liked it best of all when Jimmy's dog sat by the fire.

One day, Jimmy took his dog on a long, five-mile hike. It was a fine day and Spike liked the ride very much. All of a sudden Jimmy's dog spotted a hare and began to whine. Before Jimmy could stop him, his dog ran off as fast as he could after the hare.

Poor Spike! While Jimmy's dog ran after the hare, Spike had to hold on for dear life. On and on they went for what felt like miles. At last, the hare took a dive into a hole. After that, Jimmy's dog went back to Jimmy.

Jimmy said it was time to go home and took his dog back on the path. Spike was so tired that he dozed off and began to slide down the side of Jimmy's dog.

With a bump, Spike landed on the path and woke up. He could see Jimmy taking big strides with his dog, but they were walking too fast. Here he was, all alone, with no Jimmy and no dog for a home. Spike felt like crying.

Just then, a bike with red stripes came to a stop beside him. A boy flung a paper onto a driveway. It was Sammy, the boy who took papers to Jimmy's house! Spike did not stop to think. He took a big jump and landed slap bang next to the tire on Sammy's bike.

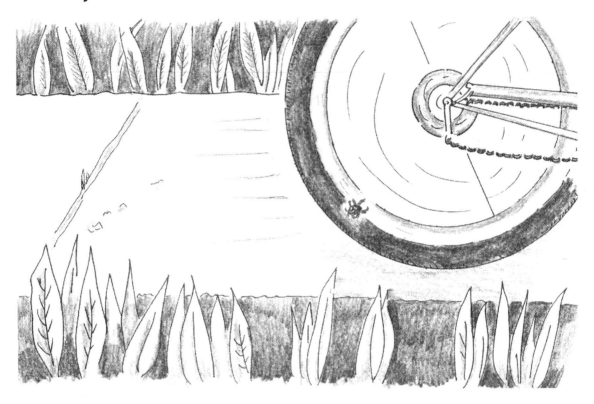

So that was how Spike the Mite got to ride on a bike. Before long, Sammy stopped his bike in front of Jimmy's house. Spike jumped off. In no time at all he was back on Jimmy's dog as he slept by the fire. After that, when Spike met the mite who became his wife, he liked to tell her about his ride on a bike.

SPIKE THE MITE
WHO HAD A RIDE ON A BIKE

WORDS TO KNOW

<u>High Frequency Decodable Words</u>

be, he, go, by, crying, all, cold, most, hold, for, her, after, see, dear, rain, day, too, took, poor, how, down, house, outside, about, walking, began, taking, before, paper, driveway

<u>High Frequency Irregular Words</u>

what, into, could, one, very, said, front, sometimes

<u>Definitions</u>

mite – a *small parasite*

hare – an *animal similar to rabbit with longer ears*

HOPE THE MOLE
WHO SNORED IN CLASS

When Hope the Mole was small, she liked to stay at home and sleep a lot. Then, when she became five, her mom and dad said it was time she went to school.

Hope was not happy at all. "I want to be at home," she said to Mom and Dad Mole. "That way I can take a nap when I want." But, she could tell from the way Mom and Dad spoke that this was no joke. Hope would have to go to school.

The next day, Mom dressed Hope in her best dress and drove her to school. Hope rode in the back of the car, feeling very sleepy and glum. She wanted so much to be at home, sitting by the fire, all snug in her bathrobe.

When Hope went into the class, she sat in the back behind

 a big mole named Billy Bone. The teacher's name was Mrs. Stone. She made lots of jokes, but Hope just wanted to doze.

When Mrs. Stone wrote on the board, Hope would close her eyes, put her nose on her desk, and doze. Billy Bone was so big that Mrs. Stone did not see that Hope was fast asleep.

Then one day, while Hope was dozing at her desk, she began to snore. Then she began to snore more and more. The whole class froze as Mrs. Stone stopped the lesson and strode to the back of the class.

"Wake up, Hope," said Mrs. Stone, in a very cross tone, but Hope just kept on snoring. Billy Bone gave her a poke, but that did not stop Hope from snoring. In fact, her snores were filling the whole classroom, and the rest of the moles were getting sore ears!

So Mrs. Stone went to the board and wrote:

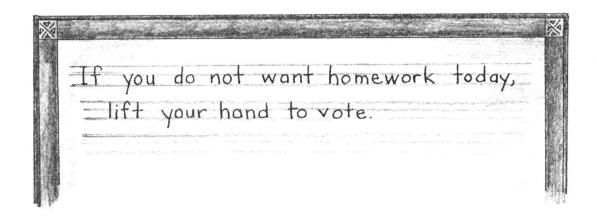

If you do not want homework today, lift your hand to vote.

Then the whole class voted for no homework, but not Hope. She was still snoring. When the bell rang, Hope woke up. When she saw what was on the board, she said to Mrs. Stone, "You played a joke on me! I am such a dope. I will do my homework and I will not doze in class anymore."

HOPE THE MOLE
WHO SNORED IN CLASS

WORDS TO KNOW

High Frequency Decodable Words

go, so, she, my, by, all, small, car, her, day, played, see, sleep, asleep, sleepy, feeling, ears, teacher, board, saw, want, about, longer, happy, became, behind, snoring, dozing, began, wrote, homework

High Frequency Irregular Words

into, said, have, you, put, very, were, one, could, would, eyes, today, school, become, anymore

Definitions

mole – a *small mammal that lives mostly underground*

LUKE THE DUKE
WHO WAS VERY RUDE

Once upon a time there was a duke named Luke. He
lived with his family in a very big home and had lots of
servants. Yet, it must be said, Duke Luke was a very rude man
indeed.

He did not say *please*. He did not thank his servants. He did not smile or wave hello to those he met in the street. Even on his children's birthdays, he did not give them hugs or gifts.

Behind his back, his family and servants said how rude he was. "He's as stubborn as a mule," Duke Luke's butler said to his cook. "I hope one day someone will teach him a lesson." Do you know what? One day someone did just that.

It happened one June day when Duke Luke was on his way home. Just as he was opening his gate, he could hear a tune on a flute. "Who is that?" he asked in a very rude tone. "If you are a servant, you do not have time to play silly tunes."

Yet as soon as he said that, Duke Luke had to stop and gasp in shock. A small elf with a flute in his hand was standing on the path next to him. "Good day, Duke Luke,"

said the elf. "I am not your servant, but why can't they play tunes on such a fine June day?"

"Be off with you," said the rude duke, "I have no time for a silly elf." Then all of a sudden, the small elf began to change. Bigger and bigger became the elf until he was as tall as a tree.

"Duke Luke," said the big elf, "It is time for you to stop being so rude." Then he snapped his fingers and waved his hands. At that, Duke Luke clapped his hands to his lips. All of a sudden, he could not speak.

In a panic, the duke ran home. His butler opened the door, but Duke Luke could not speak to him. His wife came up to him, but he could not speak to her. It was the same with his children and the rest of the servants. The elf had made Duke Luke mute.

Do you know what? All of his servants, and his wife, and his children, were very nice to Duke Luke. His children made cute gifts for him. His wife sang songs for him. His servants made big fires for him when it got chilly. Before long, Duke Luke became sad that he had been so rude to them.

Then one day, when Duke Luke was opening his gate, he could hear a tune on a flute. All of a sudden, the small elf was standing on the path. "Duke Luke," said the elf. "If I take off the spell, will you stop being so rude?"

At that, Duke Luke gave a very, VERY big nod. Quick as a

wink, the elf snapped his fingers and then vanished. The spell

was no more. Duke Luke could speak! After that, for the rest

of his life, Duke Luke was no longer rude –– and because of

that, he lived happily ever after.

LUKE THE DUKE
WHO WAS VERY RUDE

WORDS TO KNOW

<u>High Frequency Decodable Words:</u>

be, he, why, all, small, her, day, way, play, street, hear, teach, speak, please, how, cook, soon, good, bigger, hello, chilly, silly, happened, butler, stubborn, servants, indeed, being, became, before, because, behind, even, opening, ever, vanished, family, birthdays, know

<u>High frequency Irregular Words</u>

do, you, one, have, give, live, lived, said, what, very, they, what, could, there, who, once, someone

<u>Definitions</u>

duke – *a nobleman or lord*

mule – *an animal that is half donkey, half horse*

mute – *unable to speak*

JACQUELINE VINESSE

Jacqueline Vinesse holds a degree in Developmental Psychology from the University of Edinburgh and is an Orton-Gillingham trained tutor. Besides teaching psychology in Japan and South Carolina, she has spent a number of years working as a tutor and primary teacher at Camperdown Academy, Greenville, SC. She has two daughters and currently resides in France with her husband.

ELIZABETH TAYLOR

Most of her childhood years were spent in San Juan, Puerto Rico. As a child, she loved to imagine and draw--none of that has changed over the years. She never thought it would be much fun to be a "grown up", and in illustrating children's books she is able to stay young at heart. She has spent much of her life raising her own four children and teaching in elementary school.